LEARN TOGETHER
SCIENCE

MYSELF
1

Richard Dawson

A Piccolo Original
Piccolo Books

Note to parents

Welcome to this book.

Science hides behind the mysterious veils of difficulty and incomprehension – brush aside these veils and it is fun!

This book, **Myself**, contains facts, puzzles and experiments put together to give children a fun start to the world of science.

The activities in the book are similar to the science activities your child will be engaged in at school and are firmly linked to the National Curriculum. Science is the practical activity of finding out, so your child may require some help with the reading of instructions before they are able to engage in the activity.

Whether you are reading, exploring or recording, join your child and enjoy the partnership of learning together about **Myself**.

First published 1993 by Pan Macmillan Ltd,
Cavaye Place, London SW10 9PG

9 8 7 6 5 4 3 2 1

Text © Richard Dawson 1993
Illustrations by Richard Dawson

The right of Richard Dawson to be identified as author of this work
has been asserted by him in accordance with the Copyright,
Designs and Patents Act 1988.

ISBN 0 330 33009 8

Typeset by Pan Macmillan Ltd
Printed and bound in Great Britain by
Henry Ling Ltd, The Dorset Press, Dorchester

This is me

Draw a picture of yourself and label the different parts of your body by drawing a line to the right word.

head

chin

hair

eye

shoulder

neck

arm

hand

elbow

hip

waist

knee

leg

foot

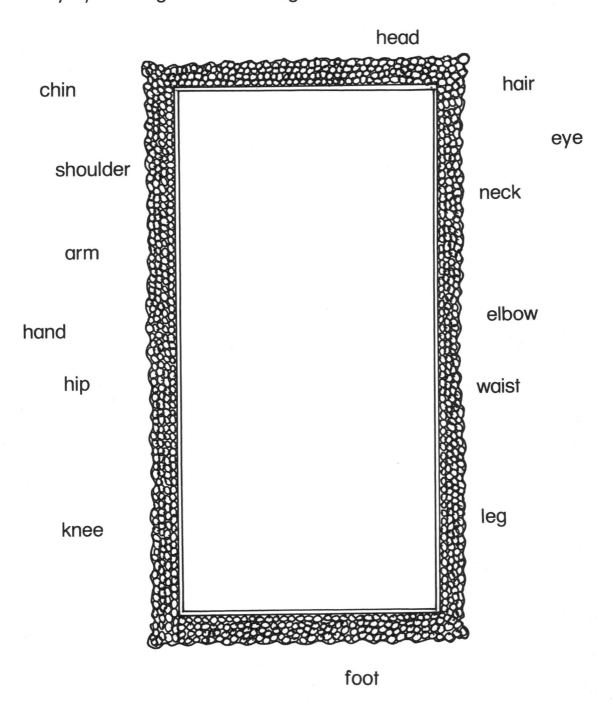

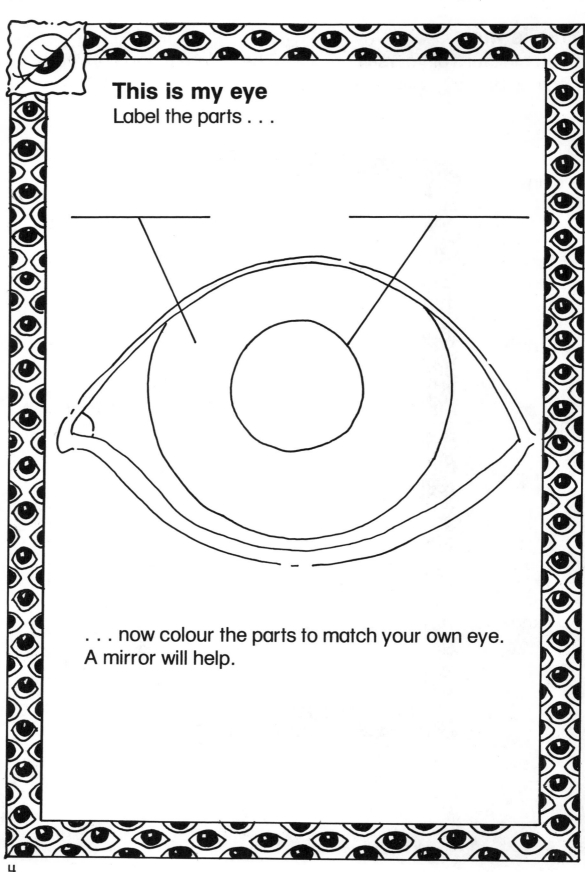

This is my eye
Label the parts . . .

. . . now colour the parts to match your own eye.
A mirror will help.

Whose eyes? 1. 2. 3. 4. 5. 6.
Connect the eyes to their owners.

Some animals have bigger pupils than others.
Do these animals have anything in common?

Pupils

Sit in front of a mirror. Close your eyes and count to twenty. Quickly open your eyes and look at your pupils.

What happened to them?

_____

_____

Why do you think this happened?

_____

_____

Fingerprints

Everyone's fingerprints are different!
There are four main types.

whorl   loop   arch   composite

Use ink or paint to print your fingerprints here.
Left hand

Right hand

Look at your prints carefully. A magnifying glass will help.
Are any of your prints the same?
What type are your prints?

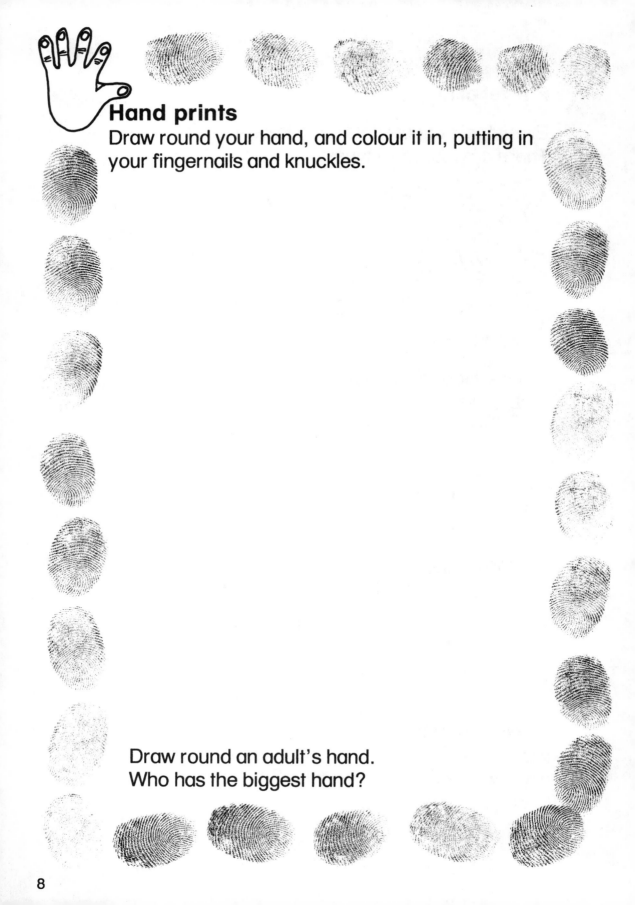

Hand prints

Draw round your hand, and colour it in, putting in your fingernails and knuckles.

Draw round an adult's hand.
Who has the biggest hand?

Seeing without our eyes

Cut out from card the letters that spell your name.

When you have finished, ask someone to blindfold you. Now see if you can 'spell' your name using your fingers!
Stick your letters here.

Which part of your fingers can feel the letters best?

How do you hear?

Put some dried peas on a stiff piece of paper.

Now tap the corner of the paper. What happens?

_____

_____

We call this bouncing movement vibration.
Put your fingers gently to your throat.
Say 'ahhhh'. What do you feel?

_____

When we speak, we make the air **vibrate**.

Ear we go . . .

The ear looks like this.

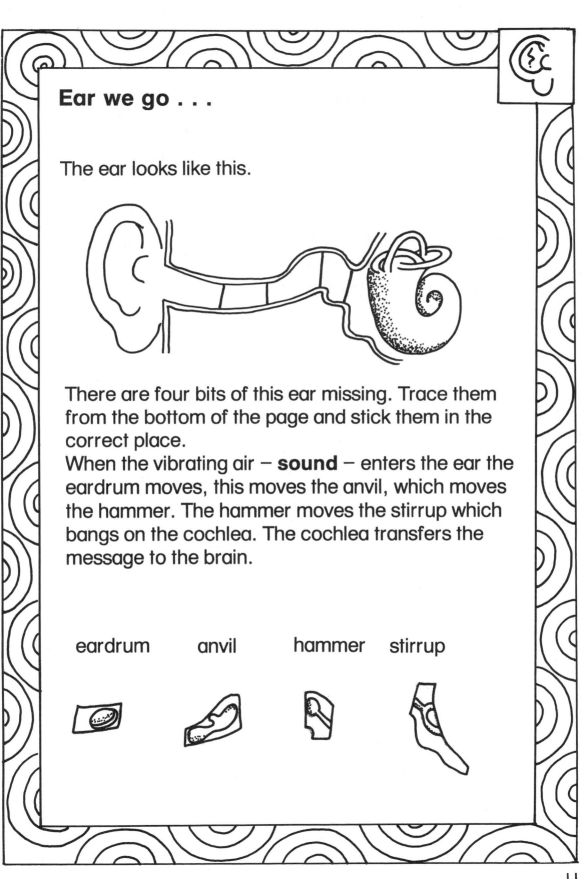

There are four bits of this ear missing. Trace them from the bottom of the page and stick them in the correct place.

When the vibrating air – **sound** – enters the ear the eardrum moves, this moves the anvil, which moves the hammer. The hammer moves the stirrup which bangs on the cochlea. The cochlea transfers the message to the brain.

eardrum   anvil   hammer   stirrup

Bumpsie daisy

The stirrup, anvil and hammer are the smallest bones in the body. Try this experiment. It will show you how the bones work.

Line up a row of people like this . . .

Now gently push the person at one end. What happens?

_____

_____

_____

_____

_____

This is how the bones move each other.

Hear, here
Can you tell where sound comes from?

Put your finger in one ear, sit down on a chair and close your eyes. Keep very still and ask a friend to move a ticking clock slowly around your head.
Shout 'stop' when you think the clock is near the ear you have blocked.
Take your finger out of your ear and try the experiment again. What happened?

_____

_____

_____

Watch a dog, a cat or a horse. They can move their ears towards sound without moving their heads.
Some people can move their ears a little. Can you?

Eyes together

Hold your pen in one hand and the top in the other.

Close your right eye and try to put the top on the pen.

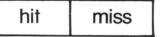

hit	miss

Close your left eye and try to put the top on the pen.

hit	miss

Open both eyes and try to put the top on the pen.

hit	miss

Balance

Lay out a skipping rope on the floor.
Now walk along it, don't fall off!

Quickly spin around fifteen times.

Now walk along the rope again.
What happened?

_____

_____

How do you think people who spin around a lot –
astronauts, ballet dancers – avoid getting dizzy?

How do you feel?
We feel with our hands.

Try this experiment. Fill three bowls with water – one hot, one cold and one lukewarm.

hot water   lukewarm water   ice-cold water

First put one hand in the hot water and one in the cold. Now put both hands in the lukewarm water. How does each hand feel?

_____

_____

_____

_____

_____

Important – do NOT use boiling water.

Crossword

Try this crossword (you know it makes sense!).

2➤ What you do with 2↓
6➤ What you do with 3↓
5↓ What you do with 1↓
7➤ What you do with 4➤
8↓ What you do with 9➤

17

Dem bones

Draw in your bones.

Strong arm tactics

Bend and straighten your arm. Can you feel the muscles?

What are they doing?

Trace these arm shapes on to strong card and cut them out.

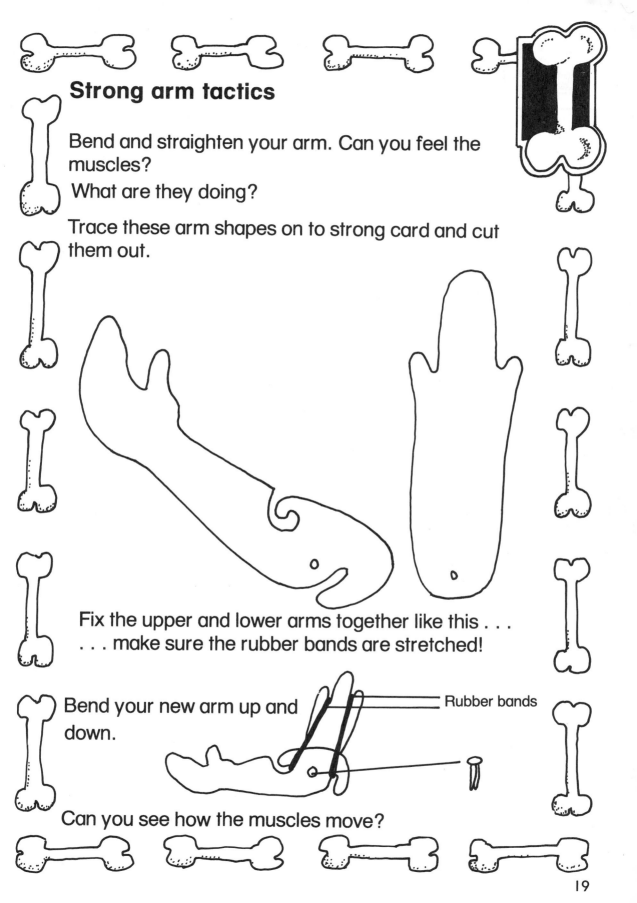

Fix the upper and lower arms together like this . . .
. . . make sure the rubber bands are stretched!

Bend your new arm up and down.

Rubber bands

Can you see how the muscles move?

Did you know?

How much do you weigh?

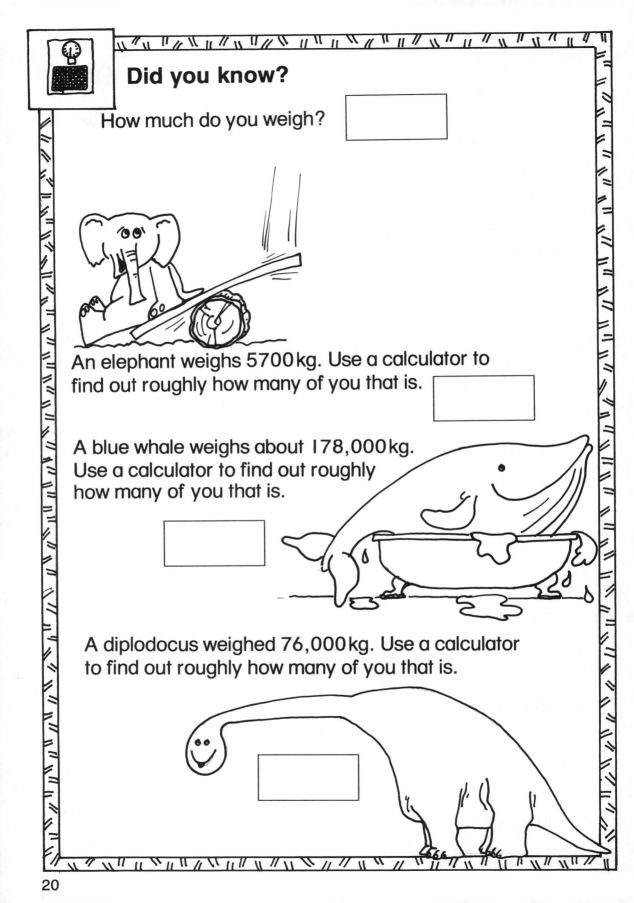

An elephant weighs 5700 kg. Use a calculator to find out roughly how many of you that is.

A blue whale weighs about 178,000 kg. Use a calculator to find out roughly how many of you that is.

A diplodocus weighed 76,000 kg. Use a calculator to find out roughly how many of you that is.

Quicker than the eye

Trace these pictures and stick one on each side of a piece of round card.

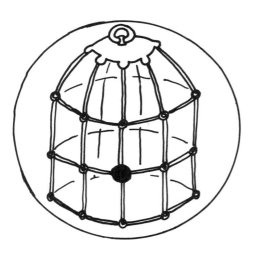 

Stick a straw to the disc with adhesive tape . . .

. . . and spin the disc in your hands!
Try making another disc using a fish and a bowl.

Hair raising!

Stand in front of a mirror.
With a hair brush, brush your hair quickly for a
minute.
Now hold the brush above your head.

Draw what happens to your hair.
Do you know why this happens?

_____

_____

_____

Body magic

Stand up straight. Ask someone to hold your hands by your side and try to lift your arms out. Keep pressing against your partner's hands until you can press no more. Relax and ask your partner to let go . . . What happens?

_____

_____

_____

_____

_____

_____

Meals

Draw a healthy meal . . .

. . . and a not so healthy meal!

Which meal would you choose?

Remember, remember

Look carefully at the picture for one minute.

Close the book and name as many animals as you can.

How quick are you?

Copy the reaction tester on to a piece of card.
You will need someone to work with.

Ask someone to drop the tester for you.

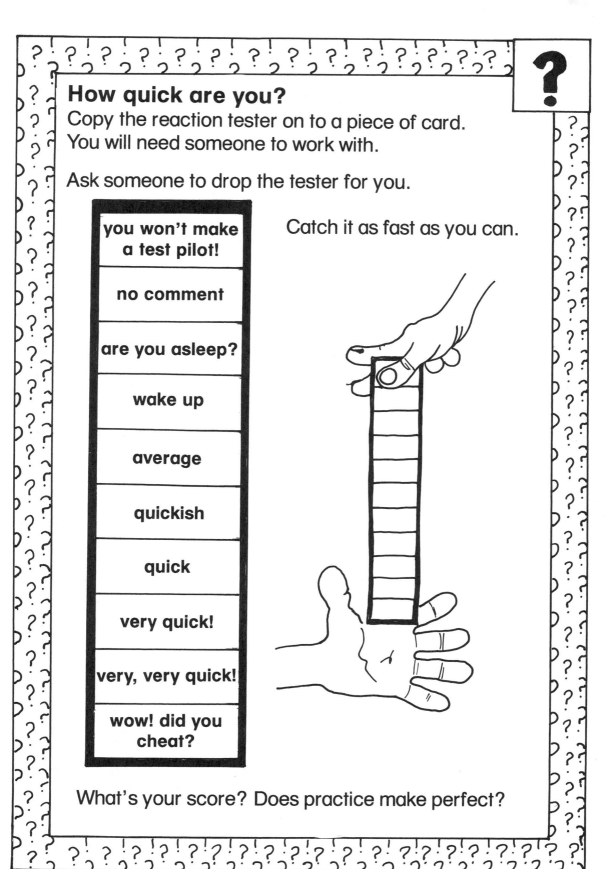

Catch it as fast as you can.

you won't make a test pilot!
no comment
are you asleep?
wake up
average
quickish
quick
very quick!
very, very quick!
wow! did you cheat?

What's your score? Does practice make perfect?

Have a wild guess

When you sneeze, the air travels as fast as

a cheetah?   **a hurricane?**   **Concorde?**

Ahhah . . . choo!

When you put your ear to a shell you hear

a whale whisper?

the sea?

the echo of your blood moving in your ear?

psst!

Your brain is made mostly of
muscle?
water?
a special grey matter?

You're tallest

before breakfast?   **at lunchtime?**

after dinner?

Heart throb

Find your pulse, it is in your wrist.
Your pulse beats with your heart.
Feel your pulse and you know your heart is beating.
Count how many beats you have in one minute.

Run as fast as you can on the spot.
Take your pulse again!

What do you notice?

_____

_____

What does this mean?

_____

_____

Dressing up

Colour the clothes that you wear on a hot day **red**, and those for a cold day **blue**!

The Big Body Wordsearch

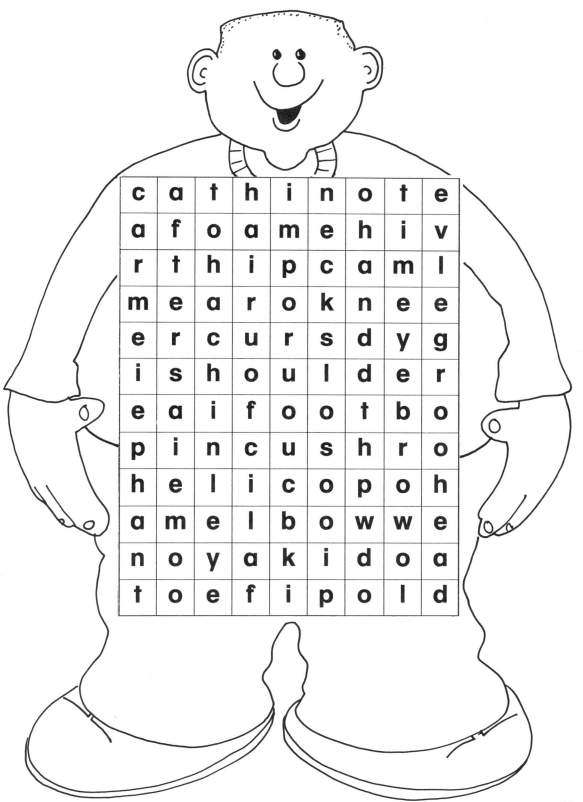

c	a	t	h	i	n	o	t	e
a	f	o	a	m	e	h	i	v
r	t	h	i	p	c	a	m	l
m	e	a	r	o	k	n	e	e
e	r	c	u	r	s	d	y	g
i	s	h	o	u	l	d	e	r
e	a	i	f	o	o	t	b	o
p	i	n	c	u	s	h	r	o
h	e	l	i	c	o	p	o	h
a	m	e	l	b	o	w	w	e
n	o	y	a	k	i	d	o	a
t	o	e	f	i	p	o	l	d

Answers

page 5   1. frog   2. chicken   3. cat   4. rabbit   5. human   6. fish

page 15   Astronauts have to practise and train to overcome it, and ballet dancers flick their heads faster than their body spins.

page 17

page 22   Static electricity that is caused by the combing has a magnetic effect upon the hair.

page 26   1. a hurricane   2. the echo of blood moving in your ear 3. water   4. before breakfast

page 29   The more exercise one does the harder the heart has to pump to get more oxygen around the body.

page 31

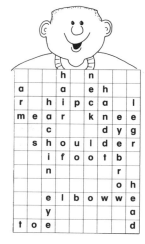